IS THE BIBLE PERSONALLY FROM GOD?

THE REAL TRUTH
ABOUT LIVING LIKE JESUS

IS THE BIBLE PERSONALLY FROM GOD?

THE REAL TRUTH ABOUT LIVING LIKE JESUS

Older Children's Workbook
Grades 4-6

JOSH McDOWELL
Dave Bellis
with Cindy Ann Pitts

Is the Bible Personally From God?

© 2006 by Josh D. McDowell and David H. Bellis.

ISBN 1932587934

Cover graphics: The Resource Agency

Undated Elective Curriculum/Primary (Grades 1 and 2)
Undated Elective Curriculum/Middler (Grades 3 and 4)
Undated Elective Curriculum/Preteen (Grades 5 and 6)

Published by Green Key Books
2514 Aloha Place
Holiday, Florida 34691

Printed in the United States of America

06 07 08 09 / 5 4 3 2 1

IS THE BIBLE PERSONALLY FROM GOD

Table of Contents

All Scripture quotations are from the GOD's WORD® Translation (GWT) unless otherwise noted.
Answers to the games, puzzles, and fill-in-the-blank activities are based on the GWT.

WHO WROTE THE BIBLE?

*Every Scripture passage is inspired by God. All of them are useful
for teaching, pointing out errors, correcting people, and training
them for a life that has God's approval.* 2 Timothy 3:16

God wants you to get to know him personally. He created you with a desire in your heart that would cause you to want to know him too. He inspired and directed over 40 people to record his message so you could have the Bible to help you know about God and what he is like. The Bible is the world's best selling book.

The Bible is a holy book. The word "holy" means "set apart for," or "by God." There is no other book in the world that can compare to the Bible. We must respect the message the Bible has for us. We need to willingly choose to obey God's words.

> **Big Truth:**
> God personally wrote and directed the writing of his Word the Bible.

Today we will learn about two Bible writers. Moses wrote the first five books in the Old Testament. The first time in the Bible that there is a reference to God telling a person to write down his message is in Exodus 17:14. Later, on Mount Sinai, God gave Moses his laws, which included the Ten Commandments.

John the disciple wrote five New Testament books, including the last book of our Bible, the book of Revelation. In Revelation 1:10–11, we read: ***"I [John] came under the Spirit's power on the Lord's day. I heard a loud voice behind me like a trumpet, saying, 'Write on a scroll what you see, and send it to the seven churches.'"*** John clearly says that the Holy Spirit of God gave him the power to write God's message down.

The Bible is Useful

Instructions: Look up each verse below. Decide if the verse is one that teaches us, points out errors, corrects people or trains people for a life that has God's approval. Then write the verse in the correct box.

Teaching	Pointing Out Errors
Correcting People	**Training People for a Life that has God's Approval**

Genesis 1:1
Deuteronomy 26:13–15
Psalm 25:12
Psalm 32:8
Psalm 56:3
Luke 6:35

Ephesians 4:6
Ephesians 4:28
Ephesians 4:32
Ephesians 6:1
Ephesians 6:13
Philippians 2:14
I John 4:16

I Wrote For God

Instructions: Read the riddles and clues below and find the identity of the Bible writer. Then fill in their name in that number's space on the next page.

1. I am a Bible writer who stood true to my belief in God, and I and three others chose not to defile ourselves with the foreign king's food. Through this show of faithfulness I was made a prime minister of the land who captured Israel—who am I? (For clues read Daniel 7:1, 28; 8:2; 9:2; 10:1, 2; 12:4, 5)

2. I am a Bible writer and king. I was the second son of David and known as the wisest man of all time because I asked God for wisdom and discernment as I began my reign as a king of Israel. I am known for writing Song of Solomon and some of the Psalms. Who am I? (For clues read 1 Kings 3)

3. I am a Bible writer who wrote the Pentateuch, the first five books of the Bible. I was a political leader and judge, and I was very privileged to be trained in the universities of Egypt. Who am I? (For clues read Exodus 34:27)

4. I am a Bible writer who was originally known as Simon before Jesus gave me my new name which means "rock." I was a close apostle of Christ; however, I succumbed to fear when he was arrested and denied him three times as he predicted. I later wrote two letters to displaced Christians which bear my name. Who am I? (For clues read Matthew 4:18)

5. I am a Bible writer who was given the important position of cup bearer to a pagan king who had conquered Israel. I soon heard about the desolation of God's temple and convinced the king to allow me to travel to Israel as a governor and begin the rebuilding of the temple and Jerusalem. Who am I? (For clues read Nehemiah 1:1)

6. I am a Bible writer who was the cousin of Barnabas and from a very wealthy family in Jerusalem. I had the privilege of traveling with Barnabas and Paul on their first missionary journey for a time, but failed to finish the journey, causing Paul and Barnabas to separate. Later I went with Barnabas on many of his missions and proved to be a faithful companion. I wrote the second book of the New Testament, the shortest of all four of the Gospels. Who am I?

7. I am probably the only Gentile (non-Jewish) Bible writer who was known as the "beloved physician" (Colossians 4:14). I was a close friend of Paul and joined him on several missionary journeys. I became a Christian after Christ's death and resurrection but was a close follower of the apostles.

8. I am a Bible writer who started out as a lowly shepherd, but became a beloved king and warrior at a very young age. Later in life I wrote very well known praise songs and poems praising God for His faithfulness and love. Who am I?

INSPIRED WRITERS

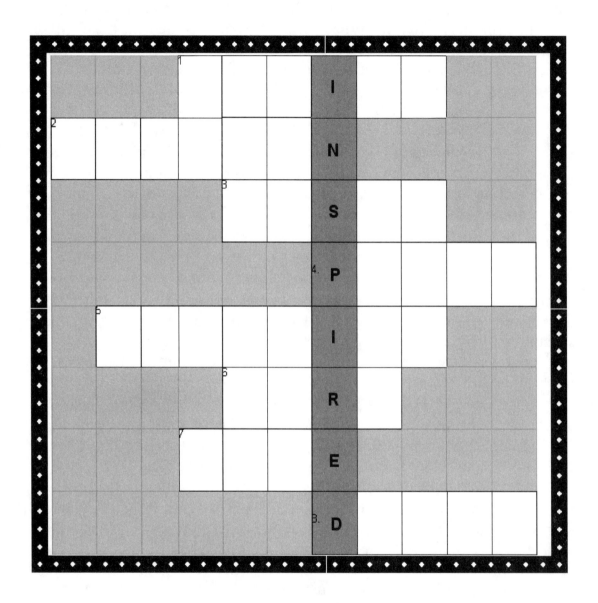

The WORD Swirl

Begin with the 'e' next to the start in the center of the puzzle and mark out every other letter after the 'e'. After all of the appropriate letters are marked out, use the remaining letters in the blanks below to spell out the verse.

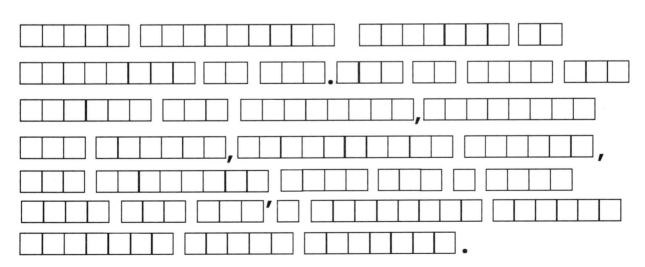

WHY GOD GAVE US THE BIBLE

*This is eternal life: to know you, the only true God,
and Jesus Christ, whom you sent.* John 17:3

God gave us the Bible so that we could get to know him and discover
what he is like. The Bible is a one-of-a-kind book; there is none like it
anywhere. There are many wonderful books about the Bible, but none of
them can take the place of God's holy Word.

The Bible is the world's best selling book. It
has been translated into more than 2,200 lan-
guages. The reason the Bible is so loved is
because its message changes the lives of the
people who read it.

> **Big Truth:**
> The Bible is God's
> way for you to
> know him so you
> can be like him.

In Genesis, the first book of the Bible, we find
the story of Adam and Eve, the first two peo-
ple God created. When God made them, they were perfect. God placed
them in a perfect world. He gave them just one rule to obey. They dis-
obeyed God's one rule for them and they sinned. Since then, all people
have sinned and need God's forgiveness.

Jesus provided the forgiveness for our sins that we need. Jesus willingly
died on a cross and took the punishment for sin on himself. If we can
believe that when Jesus died on the cross he was taking the punishment
for our sin and when he arose from the dead he was proving that he was
God and he had the power to forgive our sins, we can ask for forgiveness,
and he will forgive us and give us eternal life with him in heaven.

We can pray and ask Jesus to forgive us of our sin and ask him to come
into our life and take control of our heart and he will.

Divisions of the Books of the Bible—Playlist

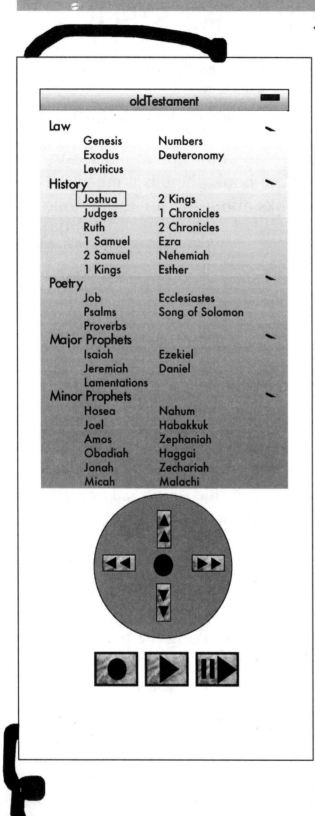

oldTestament

Law
Genesis	Numbers
Exodus	Deuteronomy
Leviticus	

History
Joshua	2 Kings
Judges	1 Chronicles
Ruth	2 Chronicles
1 Samuel	Ezra
2 Samuel	Nehemiah
1 Kings	Esther

Poetry
Job	Ecclesiastes
Psalms	Song of Solomon
Proverbs	

Major Prophets
Isaiah	Ezekiel
Jeremiah	Daniel
Lamentations	

Minor Prophets
Hosea	Nahum
Joel	Habakkuk
Amos	Zephaniah
Obadiah	Haggai
Jonah	Zechariah
Micah	Malachi

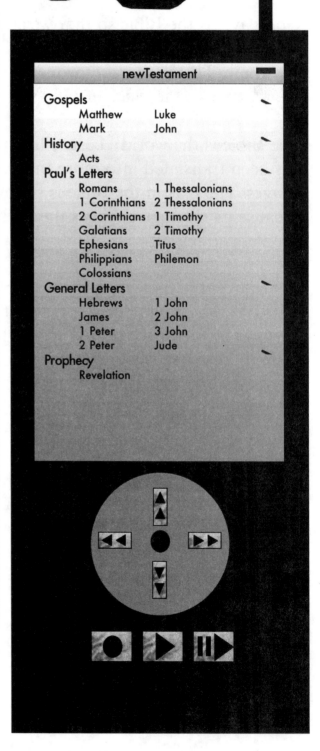

newTestament

Gospels
Matthew	Luke
Mark	John

History
Acts

Paul's Letters
Romans	1 Thessalonians
1 Corinthians	2 Thessalonians
2 Corinthians	1 Timothy
Galatians	2 Timothy
Ephesians	Titus
Philippians	Philemon
Colossians	

General Letters
Hebrews	1 John
James	2 John
1 Peter	3 John
2 Peter	Jude

Prophecy
Revelation

myWord

Search

Source	Book	Division	Old or New Testament
OldTestament	ex: Genesis	Law	Old
Law	Job		
Old Testament History	E _ _ e _ _ _ n _	Paul's Letters	
Poetry	H _ s e _		Old
Major Prophets	M _ _ t h _ _		
Minor Prophets	_ e v e _ _ t _ _ _	Prophecy	
NewTestament	Exodus		
Gospels	_ _ t h	OT History	
New Testament History	R _ m _ _ _	Paul's Letters	
Paul's Letters	Isaiah		
General Letters	_ _ k e		New
Prophecy	P s _ _ _ _	Poetry	
	_ e r e m _ _ _	Major Prophets	
	1 _ e t _ _		New
	O _ _ d _ a h		Old
	2 Samuel		
	A _ t _		New
	G _ _ _ t _ a n s		New
	_ e b r _ w _	General Letters	
	_ a b a _ _ _ _	Minor Prophets	

HE'S NOT HERE!

MATTHEW 28:5–6

"Don't be afraid! I know you're looking for Jesus, who was crucified. He's not here. He has been brought back to life as he said."

MARK 16: 6

"Don't panic! You're looking for Jesus from Nazareth, who was crucified. He has been brought back to life. He's not here."

LUKE 24:5–6

"Why are you looking among the dead for the living one? He's not here. He has been brought back to life!"

Decode the Scroll

Decode the words on the scroll below to discover the memory verse. After you have unscrambled the words write them in the spaces provided below.

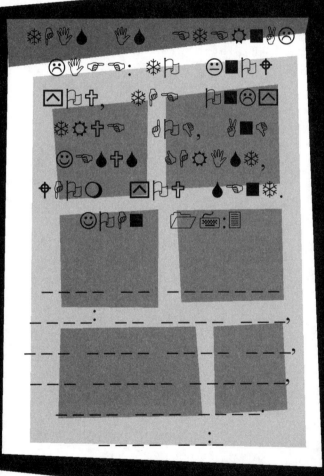

Key:
✌=A 👍=C 👎=D 👉=E 👉=F
👆=G ✊=H ✋=I ☺=J 😐=K
☹=L O=M ■=N 🏳=O ☼=R
💧=S ❄=T ✝=U ⚲=W ▱=Y
📂=1 ⌨=7 📄=3

GOD PROTECTED HIS MESSAGE

[Jesus said], "I assure you, until heaven and earth disappear, even the smallest detail of God's law will remain until its purpose is achieved." Matthew 5:18, NLT

We can trust that the Bible we have today is still the very same message that God gave to people in Bible times. God protected his message through all the years of history.

King Josiah was only eight years old when he began to rule the Israelites. He had a heart for God. For about 300 years the Israelites were ruled by kings who did not obey God. The temple was in ruins. While restoring the temple, the scrolls of God's laws were found. They were safe all along. God knew where they were because he was protecting his Word.

> **Big Truth:**
> God protected his message through history so we could know what he is like.

God used scribes who were very careful when they copied his message to make hundreds of copies of the Old Testament. God used a group of people called the Essenes to copy and hide many Old Testament scrolls in caves on the west side of the Dead Sea. These copies of the Old Testament were hidden for more than 2,000 years. All along God knew where they were and allowed them to be found at just the right time when Bible scholars could work with them best.

God guided the first Christians to take care of the New Testament. In early New Testament days, the Roman government ordered Christians to stop their work and destroy their books. Many believers were placed in prison and killed because they chose to protect God's Word. It was always God's plan to protect his words. Our Bible can be trusted to be the Word of God.

The Dead Sea Scroll

1. What are they?
223 copies of manuscripts of the Old Testament.

2. When and where were they found?
They were discovered in 1947 in caves on the west side of the Dead Sea.

3. When were they written/copied?
They were written or copied about 125 years before Jesus was born.

4. The Exciting News!
After they were translated, they had the same message we can find in the Old Testament of our Bible.

God took care of his Word so we could know him.

Session 3 Activity 1 info

14

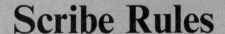

Scribe Rules

1. You may not copy from your memory. You must look at every letter. Example: If you want to write the word PRAY, copy letter-for-letter, like: p-p, r-r, a-a, y-y. Look at every letter before and after you copy it.

2. Count the number of times each letter of the alphabet occurs in the page you are copying. (Scribes had to count the number of times each letter of the alphabet occurred in each book!) Compare it to the original from which you are copying.

3. Each line you write out has to be exactly the same length as the original line you are copying.

4. Letters cannot touch each other. There has to be a space between them.

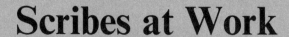

Scribes at Work

Scribe, copy Matthew 5:18 using the Scribe's Rules.

I assure you, until heaven and earth disappear, even the smallest detail of God's law will remain until its purpose is achieved.

Matthew 5:18, NLT

_____

_____

_____

_____

Matthew 5:18, NLT

Instructions: Complete the crossword puzzle and then write the completed memory verse in the space provided below.

Down
1. and earth _____,
3. even the _____ detail
5. of God's _____

Across
2. until its _____ is achieved.
4. I assure you, until _____
6. will _____

Write the verse in correct order:

_____

_____

_____

THE BIBLE SHOWS US WHAT JESUS IS LIKE

Imitate God, since you are the children he loves. Live in love as Christ also loved us. He gave his life for us as an offering and sacrifice, a soothing aroma to God. Ephesians 5:1–2

In our first session we talked about "Who Wrote the Bible" because it is important that we understand that the Bible is a Holy Book written by God. In our second session we asked, "Why did God give us the Bible?" We discovered that it was because God wanted to communicate his Truth to us. In Session 3 we learned that God carefully protected his message through all the years in history. All three of those lessons are important to the next big truth that the Bible is really all about Jesus. If we want to live a life that is pleasing to God, we must live and love as Jesus did.

Big Truth:
The Bible gives us a perfect picture of what Jesus is like so that we can know how to be like him.

There are many fantastic Bible stories about Jesus. Jesus was a teacher. He healed people of all sorts of illnesses and problems. He could bless a little boy's lunch and feed 5,000 people. He could calm a storm in the Sea of Galilee by just speaking to the winds and the waves. All these miraculous things he did proved that Jesus is God.

Each Bible story about Jesus tells us more about his character—which should become our character. Today we are going to look closely at the night before Jesus was arrested. Jesus was having the Passover supper with his disciples and he did an amazing thing to show his love for them. Jesus washed their feet! He took on the role of a servant and showed them he loved them.

What Jesus is Like

Think about what the following Bible stories tell us about Jesus' character.
Some suggested answers are: merciful, powerful, without sin,
God, compassionate.

Bible Story:
Jesus heals a paralytic.
Jesus is _____
Matthew 9:1–8

Bible Story:
Jesus pays the Temple tax.
Jesus is _____
Matthew 14:24–26

Bible Story:
Jesus walks on water.
Jesus is _____
Matthew 14:22–36

Bible Story:
Jesus and the woman at the well.
Jesus is _____
John 4:4–26

Bible Story:
Jesus feeds the 5000.
Jesus is _____
Matthew 14:13–18

Bible Story:
Jesus teaches the people.
Jesus is _____
Matthew 5

I Can Choose to Be Like Jesus

Jesus answered him, "'Love the Lord your God with all your heart, with all your soul, and with all your mind.' This is the greatest and most important commandment. The second is like it: 'Love your neighbor as you love yourself.'" Matthew 22:37–39

How can I live what this verse tells me to do in these four places? Write your answers in the squares below.

SCHOOL

PLAYGROUND / SPORTS TEAM

HOME

CHURCH

IN THE IMAGE OF CHRIST

"So I tell you and encourage you in the Lord's name not to live any longer like other people in the world. Their minds are set on worthless things." *Ephesians 4:17*

"²⁰But that is not what you learned from Christ's teachings. ²¹You have certainly heard his message and have been taught his ways. The truth is in Jesus. ²²You were taught to change the way you were living. The person you used to be will ruin you through desires that deceive you. ²³However, you were taught to have a new attitude. ²⁴You were also taught to become a new person created to be like God, truly righteous and holy.

²⁵So then, get rid of lies. Speak the truth to each other, because we are all members of the same body.

²⁶Be angry without sinning. Don't go to bed angry. ²⁷Don't give the devil any opportunity to work.

²⁸Thieves must quit stealing and, instead, they must work hard. They should do something good with their hands so that they'll have something to share with those in need.

²⁹Don't say anything that would hurt another person. Instead, speak only what is good so that you can give help wherever it is needed. That way, what you say will help those who hear you. ³⁰Don't give God's Holy Spirit any reason to be upset with you. He has put his seal on you for the day you will be set free from the world of sin.

³¹Get rid of your bitterness, hot tempers, anger, loud quarreling, cursing, and hatred. ³²Be kind to each other, sympathetic, forgiving each other as God has forgiven you through Christ." *Ephesians 4:20–32*

1. Our natural desires will _____. (verse 22)

2. Get rid of _____ because Jesus is the truth. (verse 25)

3. Handle your _____ because Jesus is in control. (verse 26)

4. Don't _____ because Jesus is _____. (verse 28)

5. Speak only what is _____ because Jesus is _____. (verse 29)

6. Get rid of _____, _____ _____, _____, _____ _____, _____, and _____. (verse 31)

7. Because Jesus is _____, _____, _____. (verse 32)

Session 4 Activity 3

23

Ephesians 5:1-2

Instructions: Decode the puzzle below by finding the number that goes with each letter and filling in the blanks below to reveal our Bible memory verse.

Note: Not all of the letters will be used.

A	B	C	D	E	F	G	H	I	J	K	L	M	N	O	P	Q	R	S	T	U	V	W	X	Y	Z
15		8		17		4	22			14			26	25	11		10		20		24		1	19	

```
"___ T A T E   G O ___ ,   ___ N C E   Y O ___   A R E
 13 21 13 20 15 20 17  4 25 18   3 13 26  8 17  19 25  7  15 10 17

T H E   C H ___ ___ R E N   H E ___ ___ O V E ___ .   ___ V E
20 22 17  8 22 13  5 18 10 17 26  22 17  5 25 24 17  3    5 13 24 17

___ N ___ O V E   A ___   C H R ___ ___ T   A ___ ___ O   ___ O V E ___
13 26  5 25 24 17 15  3   8 22 10 13  3 20  15  5  3 25   5 25 24 17 18

___ ___ .   H E   G A V E   H ___ ___ ___ ___   E ___   ___ O R ___ ___
 7  3      22 17  4 15 24 17  22 13  3  5 13  2 17   2 25 10   7  3

A ___   A N ___ ___ O ___ ___ E R ___ N G   A N ___   ___ A C R ___ ___ ___ C E ,
15  3   15 26 25  2  2 17 10 13 26  4   15 26 18   3 15  8 10 13  2 13  8 17

A ___   O O T H ___ N G   A R O ___ A   T O   G O ."
15  3 25 25 20 22 13 26 4   15 10 25 21 15   20 25   4 25 18
```

THE HOLY SPIRIT—GOD'S GIFT TO US

But when the Holy Spirit controls our lives, he will produce this kind of fruit in us:
love, joy, peace, patience, kindness, goodness, faithfulness, gentleness, and self-control.
Galatians 5:22–23, NLT

During the Last Supper Jesus had with all his disciples, he took time to prepare them for what was about to happen. Jesus knew that soon he would be arrested; he would die on a cross, rise again (because he is God), and ascend into heaven. He did not want the disciples to feel abandoned when they could no longer see him daily. So he told the disciples that God had a plan to send them a helper. The helper is the Holy Spirit.

> **Big Truth:**
>
> When Jesus went to heaven the Holy Spirit was sent to teach us how to live and love others the way Jesus loves them.

John, the beloved disciple, recorded Jesus' teachings about the Holy Spirit in the 14th to 17th chapters of John. The Holy Spirit is the third person of the Trinity. When we say that God is a Trinity, we mean that we believe in one God who relates to us in three wonderful ways. We believe in God the Father, who desires to protect and provide for us. We believe in God the Son, whom we call Jesus Christ who is the Savior of our sins. We believe in God the Holy Spirit who becomes a part of each believer in Jesus. The Holy Spirit teaches and guides us.

The Holy Spirit is a teacher, ***"However, the Helper, the Holy Spirit, whom the Father will send in my name, will teach you everything. He will remind you of everything that I have ever told you"*** (John 14:25–26). We have a personal trainer in the Holy Spirit who will never leave us. He will never give up on us. He will teach us how to live a life that pleases God.

As the Holy Spirit works in our life, his fruit will be visible in our behaviors. He will take our impatience and replace it with his patience and so on until all the fruit of the Spirit is visible in our life, and we look more like Jesus.

Jesus Teaches His Disciples about the Holy Spirit

Jesus said: "If you love me, you will obey my commandments. I will ask the Father, and he will give you another helper who will be with you forever. That helper is the Spirit of Truth. The world cannot accept him, because it doesn't see or know him. You know him, because he lives with you and will be in you" (John 14:15–17).

"I have told you this while I'm still with you. However, the helper, the Holy Spirit, whom the Father will send in my name, will teach you everything. He will remind you of everything that I have ever told you" (John 14:25–26).

"The helper whom I will send to you from the Father will come. This helper, the Spirit of Truth who comes from the Father, will declare the truth about me" (John 15:26).

"However, I am telling you the truth: It's good for you that I'm going away. If I don't go away, the helper won't come to you. But if I go, I will send him to you. He will come to convict the world of sin, to show the world what has God's approval, and to convince the world that God judges it. He will convict the world of sin, because people don't believe in me. He will show the world what has God's approval, because I'm going to the Father and you won't see me anymore" (John 16:7–10).

"When the Spirit of Truth comes, he will guide you into the full truth. He won't speak on his own. He will speak what he hears and will tell you about things to come. He will give me glory, because he will tell you what I say. Everything the Father says is also what I say, 'He will take what I say and tell it to you" (John 16:13–15).

Holy Spirit Wanted

Job Description

1. Able to _____

2. Able to _____

3. Not acceptable by _____

4. Able to _____

5. Able to _____

6. Able to _____

7. Able to _____

8. Able to _____

9. Able to _____

10. Able to _____

11. Able to _____

12. Able to _____

13. Able to _____

14. Able to _____

The Ultimate Transformer Match Up

We Can Naturally Be:	The Holy Spirit Can Provide Us With:
Selfish	Joy
Hateful	Self-Control
Sad	Faithfulness
Worried	Patience
Impatient	Kindness
Mean	Peace
Bad	Love
Cruel	Goodness
Undisciplined	Gentleness

THE FRUITS OF THE SPIRIT

Instructions: The fruits of the Spirit are LOVE, JOY, PEACE, PATIENCE, KINDNESS, GOODNESS, FAITHFULNESS, GENTLE-NESS, and SELF-CONTROL. Begin the maze at the "start" sign and work your way through, avoiding the other "fruit," to make it to the Bible where the real Fruits of the Spirit can be found.

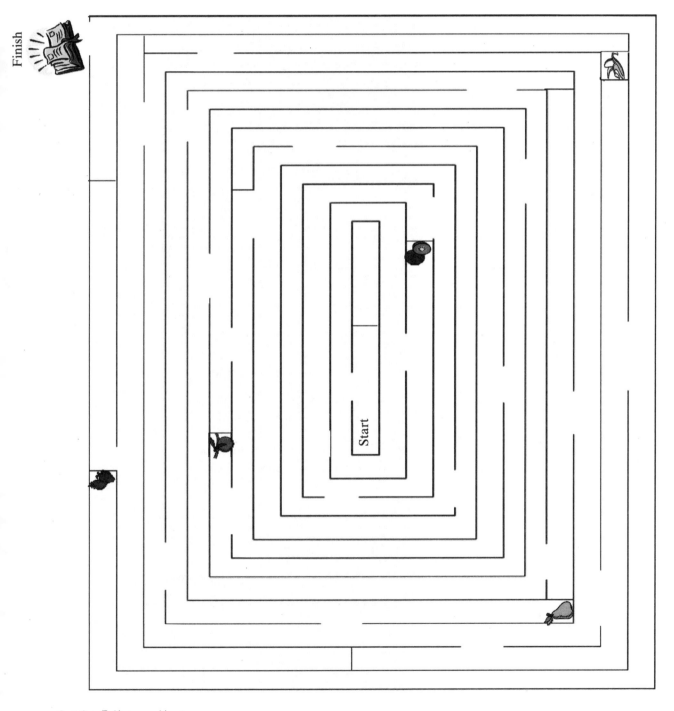

SELFISHNESS KEEPS ME FROM LOVING LIKE JESUS

"I'm giving you a new commandment: Love each other in the same way that I have loved you." John 13:34

God created us with the ability to have a friendship with him and with other people. When we decide to live our life just to make ourselves happy, we are not pleasing God. God does not want us to be selfish.

Jesus spent his life caring for others. So if we truly want to follow him we will need to put our selfishness aside and choose to care for people in the way that Jesus loves and cares for them. The good news is that the Holy Spirit will give us the power to live in a way that pleases God. The more we experience the love of Jesus, the more the Holy Spirit will cause us to want to be just like him.

> **Big Truth:**
>
> Letting go of selfishness and depending on Jesus will help you to love like Jesus loves.

One day Jesus and the disciples were walking toward Capernaum. Jesus could hear the disciples arguing. He asked them what they were arguing about. They were silent. They had been arguing about which one of them was the greatest and best. They were being selfish. Jesus told them that to be the most important person they had to be willing to be the servant of others.

Naomi was a widow. She lived in a foreign land with her two daughters-in-law. When she heard there was food again in her home city of Bethlehem, she wanted to go back there. She told her two daughters-in-law to go back to their parents' homes and marry again. One daughter-in-law did just that. But Ruth would not leave Naomi all alone in her old age. Ruth is an example of a person who was not selfish. God later blessed Ruth with a family in Bethlehem.

Just the way kids are. . . But does it please God?

Read the following case studies and think through the questions at the end.

Case 1—Teasing hurts!

Bruce was a good kid. He got along great with his parents and most kids and was an *A/B* student. There were two boys, Carlos and Nicolas, whom he really wanted as best friends. They were very popular and smart. They only made *A's*. They teased him whenever he was the last one to turn in his paper in class. They teased him in P.E. by saying he ran like a girl. They made all the other children in class laugh at him too. Bruce often felt bad inside; even though his parents were happy with his grades, he was not happy because he felt embarrassed by being teased by Carlos and Nicolas. Bruce kept doing everything he could to get Carlos and Nicolas to like him. What more could he do?

1. Who was acting in an unloving way? _____

2. Bullies sometimes use words instead of fists. A person who picks on or teases another person all the time is a bully even if he or she never hits anyone. Name some choices Bruce could make. (There could be many.)

   a. _____
   _____

   b. _____
   _____

3. How can you choose to please God in response to someone who is teasing you?

   _____

   _____

   _____

   _____

Think: If God were writing the end of this story, what would it say?

Case 2—What to do with Skittles

Kristen and Collin are sister and brother. They usually get along. One Saturday afternoon they were having a great time watching a movie. Collin remembered that he had a whole bag of Skittles in his backpack. He went and got it. Kristen saw the bag of Skittles and asked Collin to share. Collin said, "No, they are mine, and I don't have to share everything!"

1. Who was acting in an unloving way?

   _____

2. What are Kristen's choices?

   _____

   _____

   _____

   _____

3. What are Collin's choices?

   _____

   _____

   _____

   _____

Think: If God were writing the end of this story, what would it say?

COMMANDED TO LOVE OTHERS

Instructions: Search out where in the Scriptures these commands are given. One will be used twice.

1. Love each other. _____

2. Be devoted to each other like a loving family. _____

3. Show respect for each other. _____

4. Live in harmony with each other. _____

5. Accept each other. _____

6. Serve each other through love. _____

7. Be patient with each other. _____

8. Be kind to each other, sympathetic, forgiving each other. _____

9. Place [ourselves] under each other's authority. _____

10. Encourage each other. _____

SCRIPTURE BOX

Ephesians 4:32	1 Thessalonians 5:11	Galatians 5:13
1 John 3:11	Romans 12:10	Romans 12:16
Ephesians 4:2	Ephesians 5:21	Romans 15:7

MirroregamI

Try to break the code below. Write down what you think the answer is in the space provided. After you have written it down, look at the original message in a mirror to see if you guessed right.

wen a uoy gnivig m'I"
evol: tnemdnammoc
eht ni rehto hcae
I taht yaw emas
".uoy devol evah
TWG 43:31 nhoJ

_____

_____

_____

_____

We are to be mirror images of Christ!

FOLLOWING JESUS' EXAMPLE GIVES ME JOY

The LORD wants you to obey his commands and laws that I'm giving you today for your own good . . . You'll be blessed if you obey the commands of the LORD your God. Deuteronomy 10:13, 11:27

Everyone wants to be happy. Happy is a feeling that can come and go. God has planned that we could experience real joy in our heart no matter what is going on in our world. Joy comes in obeying the commandments and laws God has given us. So how does obedience lead to happiness and joy?

When we love others like Jesus loves people, we will treat them with respect and have better relationships with people. Having right relationships with people results in real joy in our life. When we do not treat others in ways that are kind and fair, we will have strife. When we make the right choices and are kind and loving to other people, we will receive more love and care from them.

> **Big Truth:**
> The more I love people like Jesus loves them, the more joy I will have.

At times you will care for others, and they will never thank you. You can still feel the joy in your heart if what you did was first to obey God's commands to love others. Obeying God always results in benefits for your own good, as our Bible verse says.

When we follow the **STEPS OF TRUTH** to make the right choices, especially in our friendships with others, we will be blessed with God's protection even if the choice was hard. We can also count on God to provide what we need. The **STEPS OF TRUTH** are:

Consider the choice. The Bible teaches us what is right and wrong. Ask yourself: What will happen if I choose to do what I am thinking about?

Compare it to God. The Bible teaches us what God is like. Ask yourself: Does what I want to do reflect God's nature? The Bible teaches us that God is love, so if I want to hurt another person, I will know it is the wrong choice.

Commit to God's way. The next step is for me to decide to do the right thing even if it is going to be hard to do or if I will be unpopular for doing the right thing.

Count on God's protection and provision. Once I do the right thing, I can know that God will protect me and he will provide what I really need. I will be blessed for making the right choice.

THE STEPS OF TRUTH

Choosing to be honest is for my own good.

Give an example of a time when you are tempted to lie, cheat, or steal.

_____

_____

CONSIDER THE CHOICE—How can you decide what is right?
List the benefits and consequences of your choices.

If I choose _____   If I choose _____
(to do what is wrong)   *(to do what is right)*

The benefits are   *The consequences are*   *The benefits are*   *The consequences are*

_____   _____   _____   _____

_____   _____   _____   _____

_____   _____   _____   _____

COMPARE IT TO GOD—What does God say? "Do not steal. Do not lie. Do not deceive one another" (Leviticus 19:11).

God is True

COMMIT TO GOD'S WAY—How can you choose to obey God in the situation about which you wrote?

_____

COUNT ON GOD'S PROTECTION AND PROVISION—How can choosing God's way protect and provide for us?

☑Check the benefits you get from your specific right choice.

God Protects Me from   *God Provides Me with*
- ☐ guilt   ☐ clear conscience
- ☐ shame   ☐ sense of accomplishment
- ☐ cycle of deceit   ☐ good reputation
- ☐ ruined relationships   ☐ trusting relationships